The Spooky night

by Frances Ann Ladd

Illustrated by Duendes del Sur

SCHOLASTIC INC.

New York   Toronto   London   Auckland   Sydney
Mexico City   New Delhi   Hong Kong   Buenos Aires

Scooby-Doo and Shaggy
went for a walk.
It was a spooky night.

They saw a light
shining on the pool.
"Scoob,
what is that light?"
said Shaggy.
Scooby howled,
"Ow-oooooo!"

Hoo-hoo, hoo-hoo.
"Scooby, did you hear
that spooky sound?"
said Shaggy.
"Ow-oooo!"
Scooby howled.
"Me, too!"
said Shaggy.

They saw a bright ball
in the bamboo.
"Scooby,
what is that ball?"
said Shaggy.
"Ow-roooo!"
Scooby-Doo howled.
Shaggy walked faster.
"Let's go in soon,"
he said.

Then Scooby-Doo pointed
at a gloomy shape.
Shaggy jumped.
"Oooh, zoinks!"
The gloomy shadow
jumped, too.

"Cool!
It's only a shadow
of my hairdo!"
said Shaggy.

"And hey, dude!
It's just the moon
we keep seeing!"

Hoo-hoo! Hoo-hoo!
"Like, I'm spooked!"